Library of Congress Cataloging-in-Publication Data

Brice, Raphaëlle.
    From oil to plastic.
    Translation of: Du petrole au plastique.
    Includes index.
    Summary: Text and pictures explain how plastic is made from oil, the problems with this nearly indestructible material, and its future.
    1. Petroleum — Juvenile literature. 2. Plastics — Juvenile literature. [1. Petroleum 2. Plastics] I. Kniffke, Sophie, ill. II. Title. III. Series: Young Discovery Library; (Series): 17.
TP690.25.B7513   1988   668.4   87-31753
ISBN 0-944589-17-0

CHILDRENS PRESS CHOICE

A Young Discovery Library title selected for educational distribution

ISBN 0-516-08274-4

Written by Raphaëlle Brice
Illustrated by Sophie Kniffke

Specialist Adviser:
Peter A. Lukacs
Chemical Engineer
B.S., M.S., Massachusetts Institute of Technology

ISBN 0-944589-17-0
First U.S. Publication 1988 by
Young Discovery Library
217 Main St. • Ossining, NY 10562

©1985 by Editions Gallimard
Translated by Sarah Matthews
English text © 1987 by Moonlight Publishing Ltd.
Thanks to Aileen Buhl

YOUNG DISCOVERY LIBRARY

From Oil to Plastic

What were men's first tools?

YOUNG DISCOVERY LIBRARY

At first, people used stones to make their weapons and tools. After a while, they discovered iron. If they made the iron very hot, they found they could beat it into any shape they liked.

Shaped flint

Axe and dagger

We don't live in the stone age, we don't live in the iron age; we live in the plastic age! Plastic is all around us.

Iron spearhead

Where does plastic come from?
It is made from oil.
Look at the picture on the right. How many plastic things can you see?

Plastic on our feet

Oil began in the sea,

long before there were even any dinosaurs walking the Earth. For millions of years, tiny little algae and minute animals called plankton drifted down to the seabed as they died.

In the beginning, sea and algae

The first sea creatures

As they sank into the mud at the sea bottom, their bodies slowly changed. First of all into a kind of sludge, and then into a thick black liquid: oil.

The age of
prehistoric animals

In ancient times, small reed boats were coated with pitch to make them watertight.

In the Middle Ages, in Mediterranean countries, boiling pitch was thrown at the enemy.

In the wonderful city of Babylon, houses were built of brick and pitch.

People have known about this black oil for a long time!

They used it when they were making boats. It is even mentioned in the Bible: the **pitch** Noah uses on the inside of the Ark,

Noah's Ark

to make it waterproof, is oil! The Mesopotamians coated their roads with pitch, just like we do today.

The Arabs had weapons with oil in them, like this grenade.

In some parts of China, people used to heat their cooking pots over holes in the ground where there was burning gas. This gas came from oil.

11

The first oil well, in Titusville, Pennsylvania, and its inventor, Colonel Drake.

Here we are in America at the time of the Wild West: oil was much sought after as a medicine. American pioneers found it by chance, digging in the ground looking for salt. In 1859, Colonel Drake sank the first oil wells.

Over the well, he built a wooden tower, with a pulley and a heavy weight. The weight broke up the rock at the bottom of the well. Suddenly, after a few weeks, oil started gushing out! It was black and as precious as gold. **The rush for "black gold" was on!**

Where do we find oil today?

Under the sea, and underground in some countries where the sea covered the land in prehistoric times.

Oil has been found in Canada and the United States, in South America, in the Soviet Union, and in Africa. There is a little oil in China, and a lot in the Middle East.

The oil companies are huge companies which find the oil, transport it, refine it and sell it.

But the biggest oil
reserves are under the sea.
There is a lot under the North Sea.
More and more people are working
to get it out, but it is very difficult.

These are the symbols of the major oil companies.

New sea monsters are riding the waves: oil rigs!

To drill right down into the seabed, the oil companies have to build huge platforms made of concrete and steel.

The rigs are built in shipyards and then towed out by big tugs to where they are needed. Oil rigs stand very high out of the sea.

In the very cold seas around Alaska, there are icebergs. They have to be towed out of the way or blown up so that they don't bump into the oil rigs.

The underwater part of a rig is much bigger even than the part which towers up into the sky. You can see the concrete holding this rig solidly on the sea bottom. Even the roughest waves can't knock it over.

Workers on the oil rigs come and go by helicopter.
You can see the helicopter landing in this picture.

A new team is arriving.

They use walkie-talkies.

The control room

Changing a drill

Life on board an oil rig

There are usually about a hundred men living on an oil rig. The work is very hard and the teams change over every two weeks or so.

Cameras automatically watch over the underwater equipment. If anything needs to be repaired, divers in wet suits go down to mend it.

Oil comes in lots of different kinds of brown as well as black. It can be runny, like syrup, or sticky, like taffy, or solid, like chocolate...

To get through the hard rock, the workers use a big **drill** made of very tough steel. Sometimes, though, the rock is too hard even for steel. Then they use a drill edged with diamonds!

The travels of crude oil.
Crude oil, straight out of the rock, isn't much good for anything. To be useful, it has to be **refined**. In the early days, oil was carried to the refineries in barrels. It is still measured in barrels to this day.

How does oil get to the refinery now? By ship, in huge **oil tankers.** Or else along enormous steel **pipelines.** There are pipelines which cross whole continents: across the icy wastes of Siberia, over the sandy deserts of Arabia, through the jungles of Central America.

Oil for flying, for driving, for heating

When it is refined, oil can be made into **kerosene,** used as jet plane fuel; **gasoline,** the fuel for cars; **diesel,** for trucks and diesel cars; **fuel oil,** for heating in houses, apartments and factories; and **naphtha,** a sort of oil which is then treated in chemical factories.

Oil for scent!

Naphtha is used for making lots of different things: detergents, dyes, fertilizers, insecticides, beauty products, scent, medicines… and **plastic.** Out of every hundred gallons of oil, ten go to make products like the ones you see below.

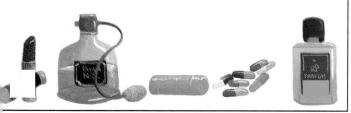

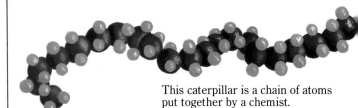
This caterpillar is a chain of atoms put together by a chemist.

The magic of chemistry

Chemists make plastics from the gas which comes from oil when it is heated. Everything in the universe is made up of tiny particles of matter called **atoms.** Atoms lock together to make all natural things, just as Lego bricks lock together. And, just like Lego, the atoms fit in a different order to make different things. Chemists have discovered how to take oil atoms apart and lock them back together again in a new order, to make thousands of different atom caterpillars. There are as many different kinds of these caterpillars as there are different kinds of plastic.

The chemist is looking through a microscope.

Plastic is a chameleon!
It can pretend to be almost anything: wood, glass, wool, metal, rubber…It is less breakable than glass, and can be clear or opaque, rigid or flexible film. It is lighter than metal; you can find it, solid and shiny, all over your house and school. Almost all toys are made of plastic.

Plastic can keep out heat or cold.
It can stand up to being knocked about. It can make soft warm material, or a waterproof fabric which keeps the rain off.

1.
The cotton which keeps us warm in winter and
cool in summer, comes from the seeds of the cotton plant.

3.
Wood comes from forests, rubber comes from the sap of a
tree. But there are an awful lot of people in the world!

2.
For thousands of years, people have used wool from sheep and leather from cattle.

4.
Nature would run out of all these things if we turned to it for everything. That's why we need plastic.

When you are in a big department store, try and find all the plastic things: bags, pens, brushes, shoes, plugs...

Look for the different kinds of plastic:
acrylic, nylon, cellophane, polyester,
polystyrene. They all come from oil.

1. These plastic granules are going to be made into something. The granules are pushed into an **injection mold.** They are heated up to make them melt.

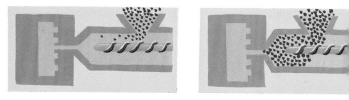

3. **Heat molding:** plastic powder is tipped into a warm mold. The mold is closed.

5. What about hollow things? They are **blown:** a tube of hot plastic is put into a mold. The mold is shut, and compressed air is blown into the tube.

2. Then the hot liquid is injected into the mold. After it cools, the mold is opened: it has made some Lego.

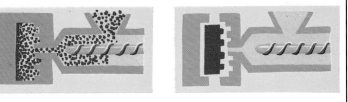

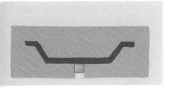

4. When the mold is opened, a bowl appears, and is pushed out from the bottom by an ejector.

6. The tube swells up like a balloon and presses against the sides of the mold. The mold is opened: it has made a bottle.

What happens to the tons of plastic we throw out every day?
They stay there!
Natural things decay, they get washed away by the sea, and break down into the earth and feed it.
But plastic doesn't! Even setting fire to it isn't the answer: it flares up and gives off a thick, poisonous black smoke.

But it is possible to purify the smoke and so a lot of plastic waste can be burned to create heat and energy. And plastic bottles can be melted down and the plastic used again.

The plastic of the future

Plastic is playing a part in the conquest of space. Plastics can be made which are ten times harder than steel and which can stand up to the highest temperatures. That is why rocket heads and fuel tanks are made of plastic.

Computers are encased in plastic.

Plastic credit cards are used in place of money.
Dentists are using plastic more and more; and surgeons are using it too, to replace all sorts of parts of the human body: heart valves, arteries, joints...
There are new plastics being made all the time, and new things being made with them.

When you play in the bathtub,
  what do you use?
Plastic toys, made to amuse!

A shovel and pail,
  a rubber-ducky toy.
All made of plastic
  for you to enjoy.

Allison Kate Dillon

Index

Books of Discovery for children five through ten...

Young Discovery Library is an international undertaking — the series is now published in nine countries. It is the world's first pocket encyclopedia for children, 120 titles will be published.

Each title in the series is an education on the subject covered: a collaboration among the author, the illustrator, an advisory group of elementary school teachers and an academic specialist on the subject.

The goal is to respond to the endless curiousity of children, to fascinate and educate.